Essential Audition So[ngs]

Female Vocalists *movie hits*

Series Editor: Anna Joyce

Editorial, production and recording: Artemis Music Limited

Design and Production: Space DPS Limited

Published 2001

IMP

International MUSIC Publications

International Music Publications Limited
Griffin House 161 Hammersmith Road London W6 8BS England

RESPECT THE VALUE OF MUSIC

Because You Loved Me

Backing

Words and Music by Diane Warren

Can't Fight The Moonlight

Moderately slow ♩ = 98

Words and Music by Diane Warren

1. Un - der a lov - er's sky, gon - na be with you, and no
2. There's no es - cape from love. Once the gen - tle breeze weaves

one's gon - na be a - round. If you think that you won't fall, we'll just wait
its spell up - on your heart, no mat - ter what you think, it won't be

© 2000 & 2001 Realsongs, USA
EMI Music Publishing Ltd, London WC2H 0QY

Chain Of Fools

Backing

Words and Music by Donald Covay

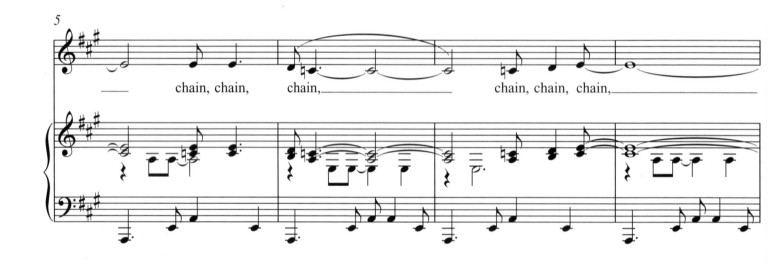

Diamonds Are Forever

Words by Don Black
Music by John Barry

Lyrics:

Dia - monds are for - ev - er,_____ they are all I need to please me,

_____ they can stim - u - late and tease me,_____ they won't leave in the night, I've no

Fame

Words by Dean Pitchford
Music by Michael Gore

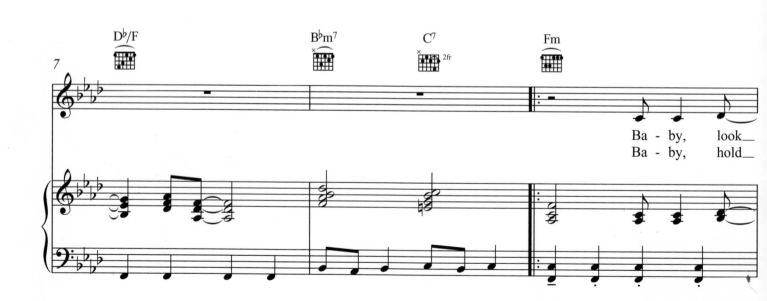

Ba - by, look___
Ba - by, hold___

For Your Eyes Only

Words by Michael Leeson
Music by Bill Conti

I nev - er felt un - til I looked at you._____ 1. For your eyes
But you won't need to read be - tween the lines._____ 2. For your eyes

on - ly,_____ on - ly for you._ You'll see what no - one else can see,
on - ly,_____ on - ly for you._ You see what no - one else can see,

now I'm break - ing free. For your eyes on - ly,_____ on - ly for you._ The
now I'm break - ing free. For your eyes on - ly,_____ on - ly for you._ The

How Do I Live

Words and Music by Diane Warren

Backing

Nobody Does It Better

Words by Carole Bayer Sager
Music by Marvin Hamlisch

G G7/B C Cm
14
but like hea - ven a - bove_ me,___ the spy who loved_ me___ is
that keeps me from run - nin'___ but just keep it com - in'___
B7 E7(b9) Am7 D7
1. G
16
keep - in' all my se - crets safe to - night.
how'd you learn to do the things you
2. G C Cm
18
do? And no - bo - dy does_ it

The Rose

Backing

Words and Music by Amanda McBroom

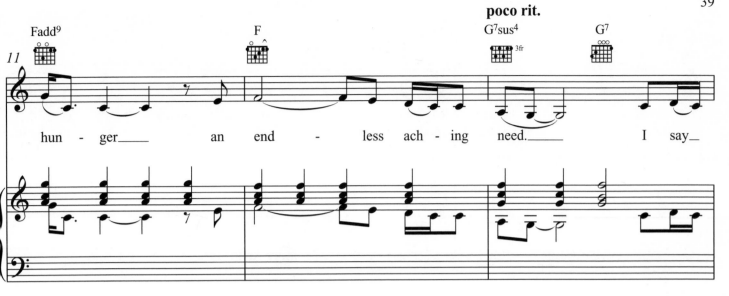

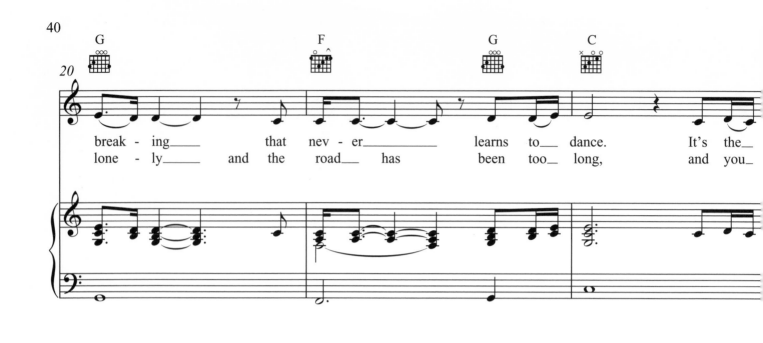

break - ing_____ that nev - er_____ learns to__ dance. It's the__
lone - ly_____ and the road__ has been too_ long, and you__

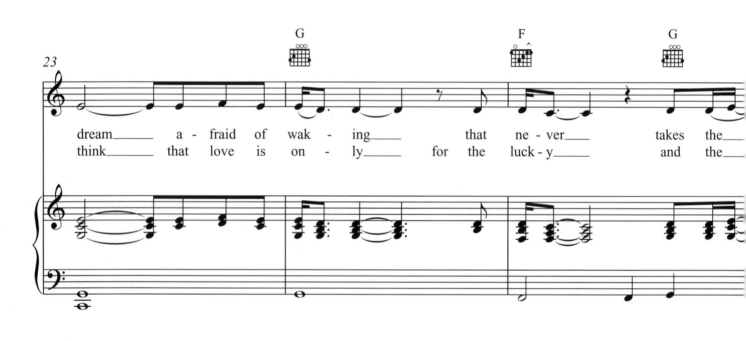

dream_____ a - fraid of wak - ing_____ that ne - ver____ takes the__
think_____ that love is on - ly_____ for the luck - y_____ and the__

___ chance. It's the__ one_____ who won't be ta - ken___ who
___ strong, just re - mem - ber in the win - ter_____ far be-

Backing

Take My Breath Away

Words and Music by
Giorgio Moroder and Tom Whitlock

Moderately slow ♩ = 96

1. Watch - ing ev - ery mo - tion in_____ my fool - ish lov - er's game;_____
2. Watch - ing, I keep wait - ing, still_____ an - ti - ci - pat - ing love,_____
3. *see block lyrics*

— on this end - less o - cean, fi-
— nev - er he - si - tat - ing to_____

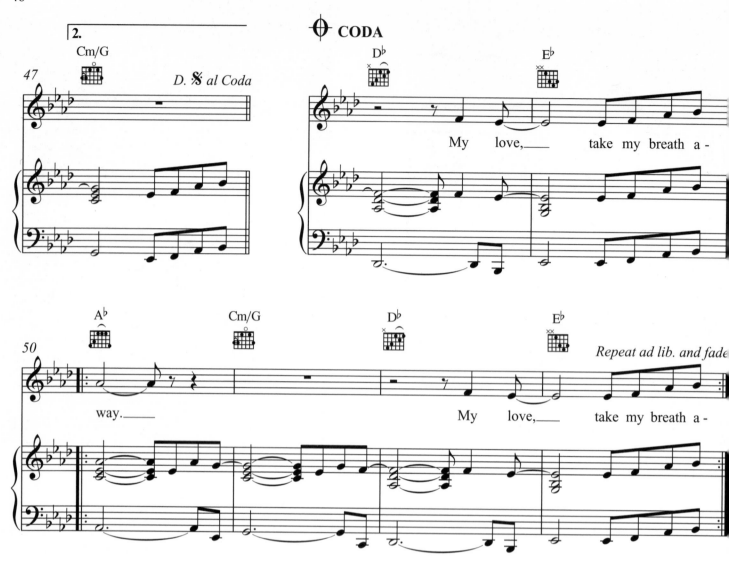

3. Watching every motion in this foolish lover's game;
   Haunted by the notion somewhere there's a love in flames.
   Turning and returning to some secret place inside;
   Watching in slow motion as you turn to me and say,
   "Take my breath away."

Printed by Halstan & Co. Ltd., Amersham, Bucks., England   6/01